© 2019 MARVEL

MASK & PUZZLE FUN

MARVEL CAPTAIN MARVEL: MASK & PUZZLE FUN
A CENTUM BOOK 978-1-912396-62-7
Published in Great Britain by Centum Books Ltd
This edition published 2019
1 3 5 7 9 10 8 6 4 2

MARVEL

© 2019 MARVEL

Centum Books Ltd, 20 Devon Square, Newton Abbot, Devon, TQ12 2HR, UK.

books@centumbooksltd.co.uk

CENTUM BOOKS Limited Reg. No. 07641486

A CIP catalogue record for this book is available from the British Library.

Printed in China.

centum

SOLVE the energy spiral! Write the answers in the grid.

1. Goose is this type of animal. (3)
2. The planet where Vers was captured. (5)
3. Skrulls are not human, they are _____ .(5)
4. S.H.I.E.L.D. agent _____ Fury. (4)
5. The Starforce unit are warriors of this race. (4)
6. Captain Marvel can fire _____ blasts from her hands. (6)
7. Vers' mentor and the commander of Starforce. (3-4)
8. The Earth force that pulls things towards it. (7)

The **last** letter of one answer is the **first** letter of next.

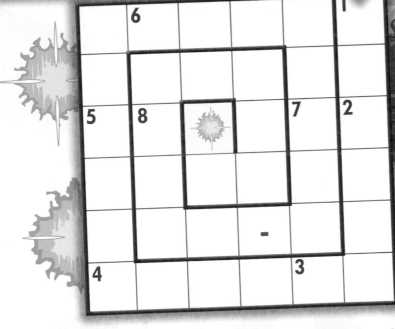

UNSCRAMBLE the letters for Captain Marvel's name as a US Air Force pilot.

S V A A E O C R D L N R

_ _ _ _ _ _ _   _ _ _ _ _ _

Answers on **PAGE 48**

COPY this image of Captain Marvel using the grid as a guide, then **COLOUR** her in.

List Captain Marvel's super powers!

_____

_____

_____

Draw lines to MATCH THE PAIRS.
Which Captain Marvel doesn't have an exact match?

COLOUR in the odd image of Captain Marvel.

Answers on
PAGE 48

Create a **NEW MEMBER** for the elite Kree warrior unit – Starforce.

NAME: _____

POWERS: _____

SPECIAL SKILLS: _____

ORIGIN STORY: _____

_____

_____

Draw your warrior, ready for battle.

Complete the names of the **STARFORCE** members.

THE STAR LETTERS WILL REVEAL THE SECRET TO THEIR SUCCESS.

_ _ _ I _ I _ _

Answers on **PAGE 48**

Carol Danvers had one true believer from the start – a tabby cat.
Can you **SPOT SIX DIFFERENCES** in the bottom picture?

What is the
cat's name?

_ _ _ _ _

Answers on
PAGE 48

Nick Fury has an urgent message for Captain Marvel. **CRACK THE CODE** by finding the letter where the **number row** and **symbol column** meet in the grid

	🍪	🌙	✦	★	📐	☀	🪐	◉
15	Z	W	A	L	M	G	T	O
14	A	S	N	W	O	I	R	G
13	N	I	X	L	T	A	O	L
12	R	V	E	V	X	N	Y	H
11	M	B	K	C	E	T	S	K
10	G	D	P	G	O	E	V	R
9	O	R	J	P	L	W	P	F
8	V	C	Q	A	D	Z	G	M
7	R	U	O	K	L	M	V	L
6	U	S	E	P	I	U	N	J
5	V	L	B	S	T	K	H	J
4	L	Q	I	G	O	N	O	K
3	T	W	N	W	F	G	N	M
2	A	R	U	S	V	U	P	U
1	M	E	T	K	W	P	Y	W

Two words are completed to get you started.

🌙14 ★1 ◉10 ☀6 ★13 ★15
☐ ☐ ☐ ☐ ☐ ☐

◉13 🪐4 ✦2 ◉6 🍪3 🌀10
M **O** **V** **I** **N** **G**

✦13 ✦7 ☀9 🍪14 🌙9 ✦8 ★2 🪐2 ◉7 ★8 🍪13 ☀10 ✦1
T **O** **W** **A** **R** **D** **S** ☐ ☐ ☐ ☐ ☐ ☐

🪐5 ✦15 ✦9 🍪2
☐ ☐ ☐ ☐

8

Answers on **PAGE 48**

Yon-Rogg is commander of the Starforce unit. Create a **NEW UNIFORM** for the Kree warrior.

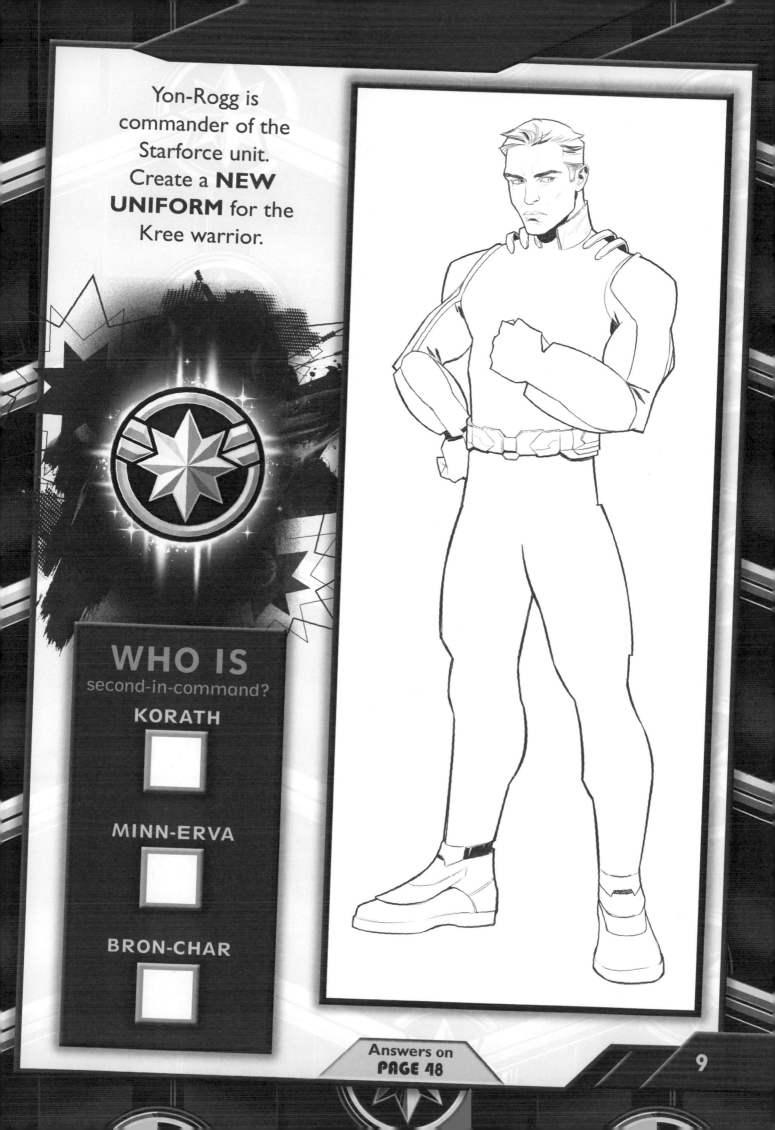

WHO IS
second-in-command?

KORATH

MINN-ERVA

BRON-CHAR

Answers on
PAGE 48

Get training for Starforce by solving these **MEGA SPACE SUMS**.

Add up all the numbers you identified – what's the full force number?

Answers on **PAGE 48**

Captain Marvel is chasing the Skrulls across the galaxy. Use the key to **FOLLOW THE PLANETS** through the grid to help her catch them!

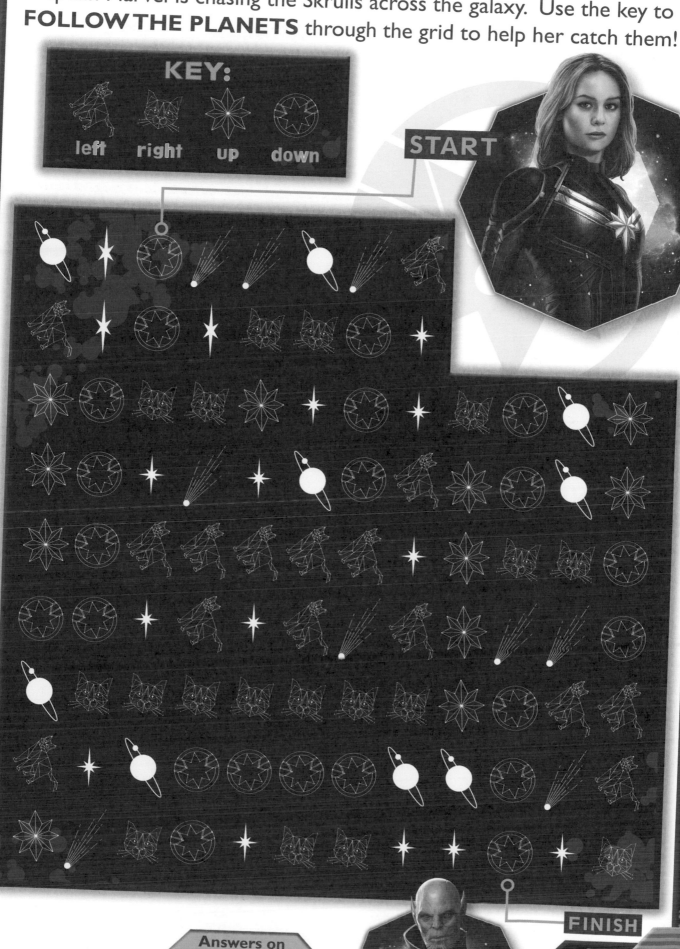

Answers on **PAGE 48**

Help Captain Marvel blast through and find the **HIDDEN WORDS**. Look up, down, forwards, backwards and diagonally!

YONROGG   MINNERVA
BRONCHAR   ATTLASS   KORATH
HALA   HELION   SKRULL

```
N A C B L O N N O K U T B H Y Y
T H K Y O I S N A M B R L U L A
M A Y K Q S R U Y L A A N I L C
C L H R A G S I I H R Y Y N B V
A A L L T G I G C A C N Y A H U
E Y T O E T C N U B S B O N M E
Y T K E K S O H N H B A N M U Y
A Y B M B R V E S R M U R H O L
T G R V B O L L C A K B O M H K
N E S M S G H I Y U G A G I L A
V T M N R T B O R N Y L G N I T
H L H I A M K N B U N U G N A A
U U U R R A R E C V H L S E Y L
N A O R O L L U R K S R G R T O
L K A N T E L K M Y I H B V H S
U M L S V N V H C I M K S A E M
```

TALOS is still hiding in the grid! Find him fast.

Answers on **PAGE 48**

What other words can you make from 'CAPTAIN MARVEL'?
BATTLE THE CLUES to find out.

CAPTAIN MARVEL

1 A drawing that can show you the way. _ _ _

2 A shelter carved into rock. _ _ _ _

3 Another word for story. _ _ _ _

4 When something is close by. _ _ _ _

5 When you gain new knowledge. _ _ _ _ _ _

6 If you stay in the same place. _ _ _ _ _ _ _

Can you make any more words from
'CAPTAIN MARVEL'?

_____   _____

_____   _____

_____   _____

Answers on
PAGE 48

This sneaky shape-shifter is up to his old tricks. Can you **SPOT** the real Talos?

HINT: He's different from all the others.

A

B

C

D

E

F

G

If you could shape-shift, **WHAT** or **WHO** would you become?

_____

14

Answers on **PAGE 48**

Pick from the word list to answer these **TRIVIA QUESTIONS**.

1. What is the colour of the Skrulls' skin? _____

2. Carol Danvers was a pilot - but for which military branch? _____

3. What part of Vers's body was injured in battle? _____

4. Which Starforce member likes to joke around? _____

5. What's the name of a planet at war with the Kree? _____

6. Who is Vers the Kree's mentor? _____

GREEN

ATT-LASS

LEG

AIR FORCE

XANDAR

YON-ROGG

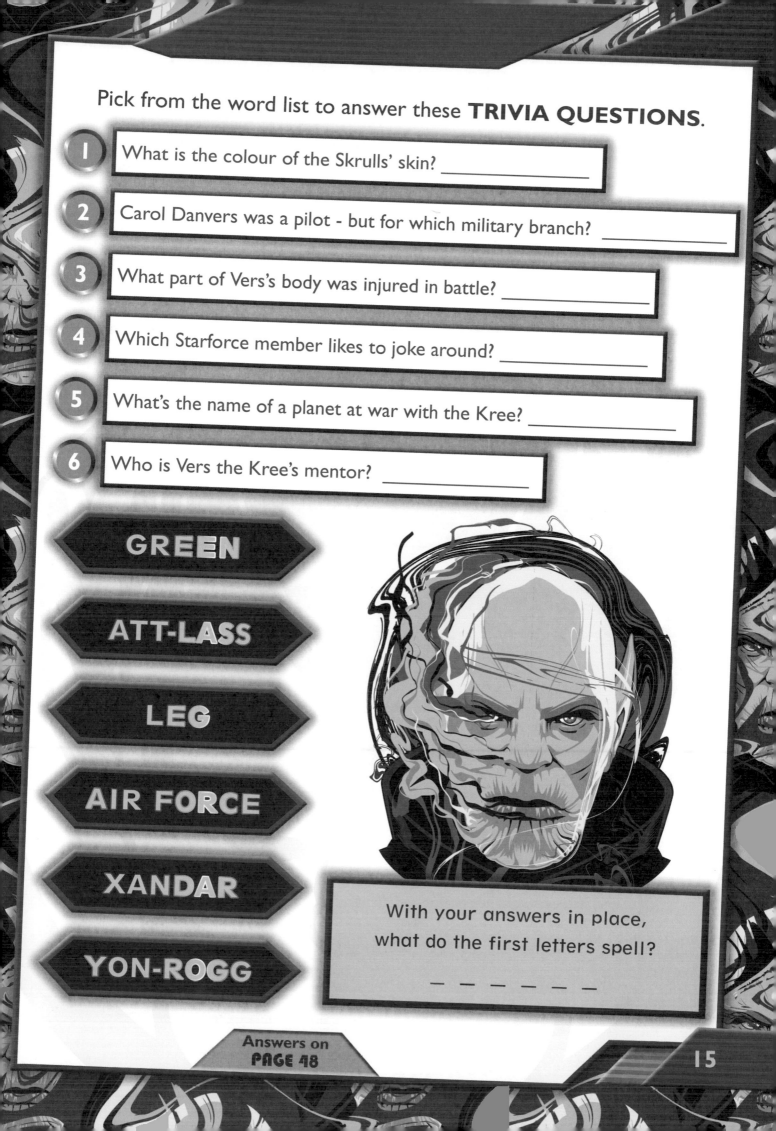

With your answers in place,
what do the first letters spell?

_ _ _ _ _ _ _

Answers on **PAGE 48**

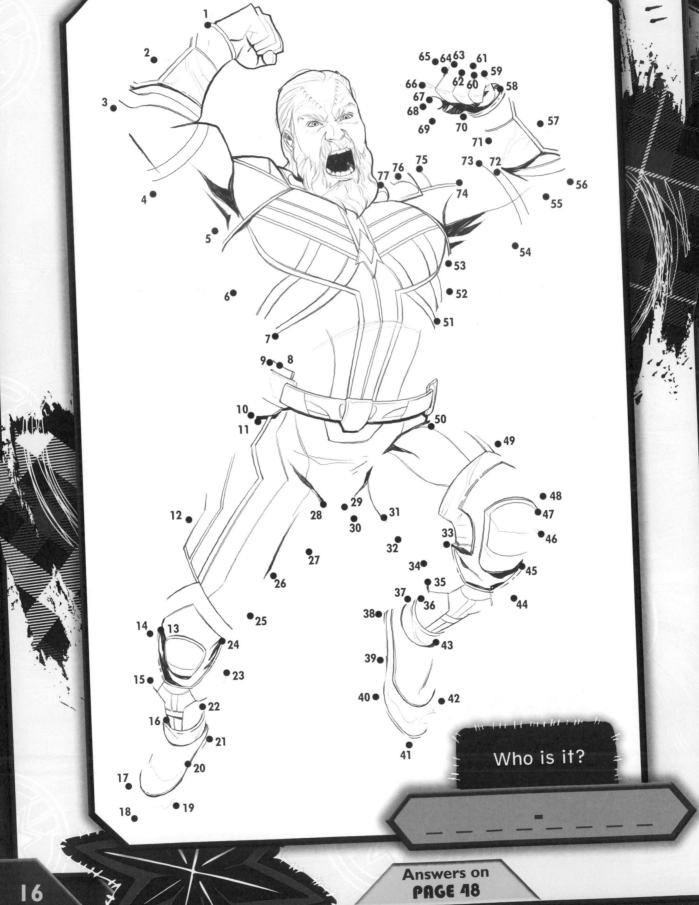

Who is it?

_ _ _ _ _ _ _ _ - _ _ _ _

16

Answers on
PAGE 48

Read the list of super skills below and **MATCH** them to the characters.

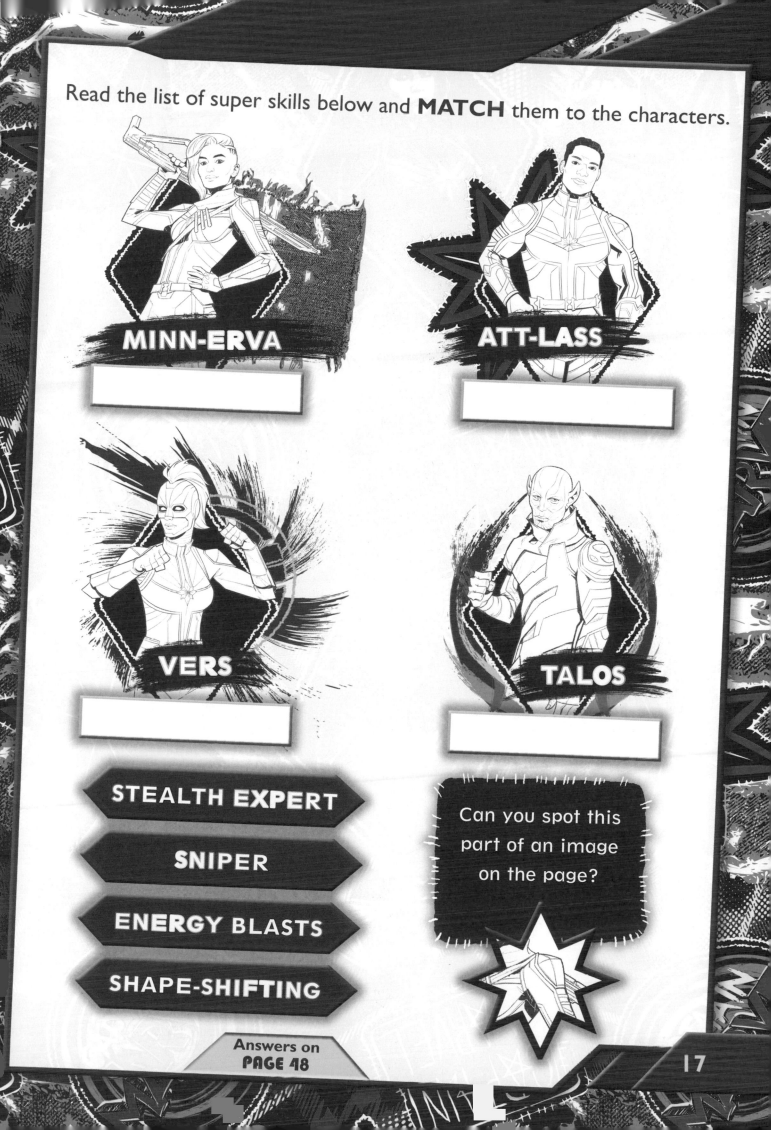

MINN-ERVA

ATT-LASS

VERS

TALOS

STEALTH EXPERT

SNIPER

ENERGY BLASTS

SHAPE-SHIFTING

Can you spot this part of an image on the page?

Answers on
PAGE 48

Prepare your **CAPTAIN MARVEL MASKS** for battle!

WHAT TO DO:

* Pop the masks out of the card pages.

* Grab your pens and colour in the Talos mask.

* Tie string or elastic into the holes provided.

* Find a friend and put on the masks.

YOU'RE READY FOR A KREE VS SKRULL BATTLE!

Pop out your energy blasts ready for battle!

SKRULL AND SEEK

Here are some intergalactic games to play when you're wearing your masks!

✴ Captain Marvel counts to 20 while Talos hides. When the time is up, hunt down that sneaky alien! When you find him, place an energy blast in that hiding spot (which means it can't be used again). Now swap masks to switch roles and play again.

TRACK THE CAPTAIN

Add sticky tack to the back of your energy blasts and leave a trail of blasts leading to your secret hideaway. Can Talos find it?

MARVEL MIND GAME

✴ Stand in battle pose and prepare for attack! Work through the letters of **CAPTAIN MARVEL**'s name by taking turns to say a word that begins with that letter. For example, '**COMIC**', '**AWESOME**', '**PHOTON**', and so on. When you get to 'L' start again at 'C'.

✴ You each get three energy blast lives. If you **pause, can't think of a word** or **repeat a word**, you lose an energy blast. The first person to lose all of their energy blasts is out of the battle!

SOLVE THE CLUES and work out who's in stealth mode.

1. I train hard and I'm a top warrior.

2. I speak my mind and some people think I'm too tough.

3. I am Vers's Starforce rival.

4. I always have my team's backs.

5. I am a sharp shooter.

The answer is

_____ .

How many letters are in this character's name?

Answers on PAGE 48

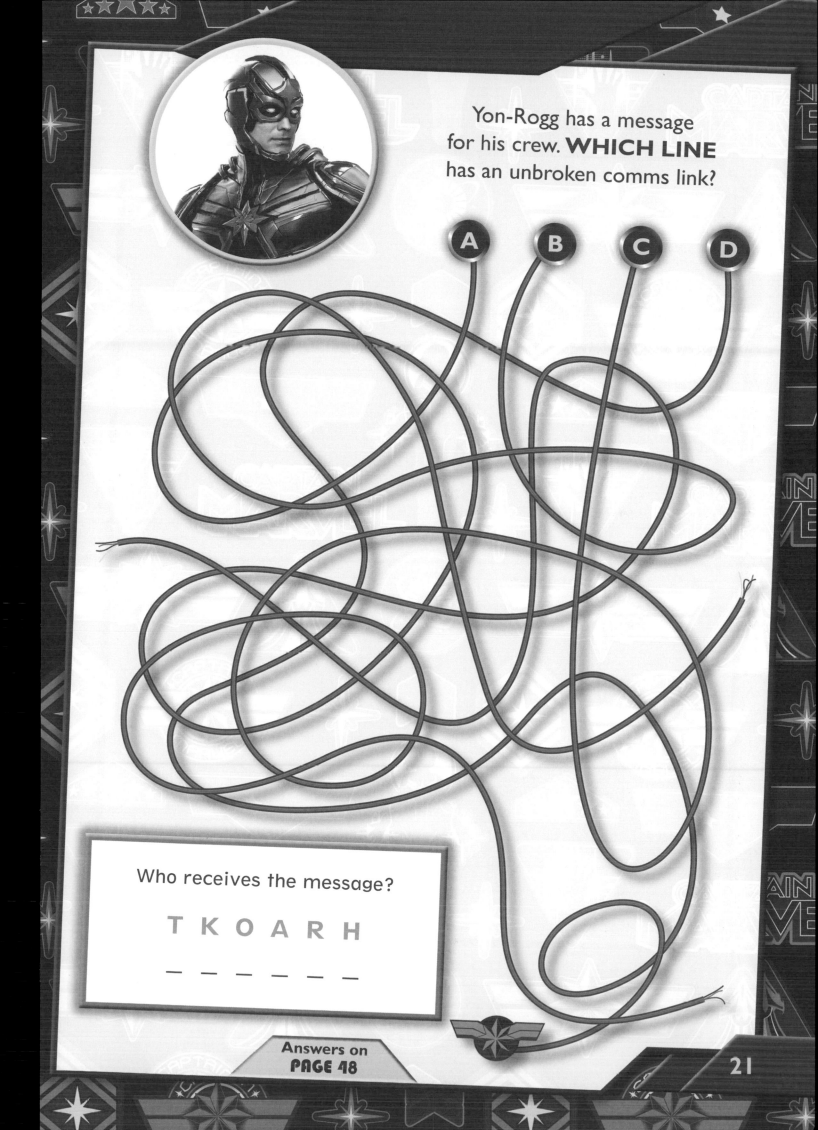

Yon-Rogg has a message for his crew. **WHICH LINE** has an unbroken comms link?

A B C D

Who receives the message?

T K O A R H

_ _ _ _ _ _

Answers on **PAGE 48**

CREATE A WEAPON worthy of the ultimate Kree warrior.

Label the parts.

Weapon name

The Starforce unit is on a night mission. Which one is which?

M_____

K_____

_____ R

_____ S

Which Starforce member is missing?

_____ G

Answers on
PAGE 48

Draw lines to connect the **MATCHING** commanders.

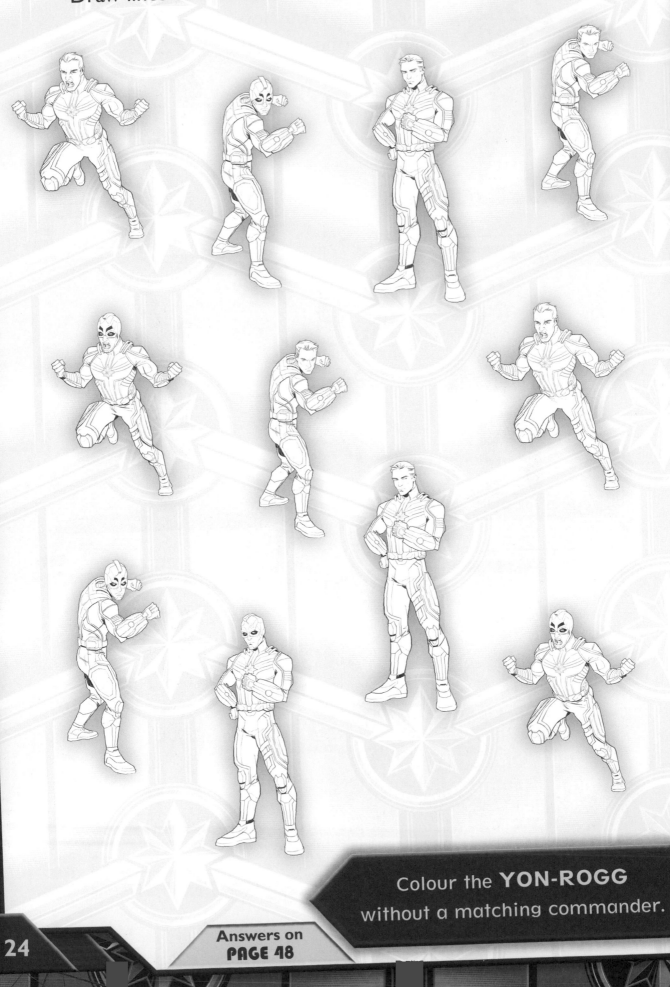

Colour the **YON-ROGG** without a matching commander.

Answers on
PAGE 48

Write some **SAYINGS** for the Starforce team!

HOW WOULD THEY REACT TO DANGER?

WHAT WOULD THEY SAY TO A SKRULL?

25

TRACE and **FINISH** the picture of Att-Lass as he tracks a Skrull.

Att-Lass loves to joke. What's your favourite joke?

Give your mind a warrior workout and solve the **CROSSWORD** clues.

ACROSS

3. Carol _____, US Air Force pilot.

5. _____ Force, the elite Kree unit.

7. To run fast at the enemy.

8. A planet that Captain Marvel wants to save.

10. Monica is a _____ of Carol Danvers.

11. S.H.I.E.L.D. agent Nick _____.

12. Torfa is a _____.

DOWN

1. Creatures from outer space.

2. Work out and practise.

4. A skill of the Skrulls.

6. Part of a plane.

9. A ship does this to go backwards.

Answers on **PAGE 48**

COUNT THE CAPTAIN MARVELS! How many times does our hero appear on the page?

Write the answer here.

Answers on PAGE 48

Prepare for Starforce **MEMORY TRAINING**.

Look carefully at this page and remember as many **characters** and **symbols** as you can.

Circle the pictures that **MATCH** those on the previous page.

NO PEEKING BACK TO THE PREVIOUS PAGE!

Which picture shows Captain Marvel's badge?

Answers on **PAGE 48**

Test the Starforce team's competitive edge and pick who you think would **BE THE BEST**!

Competition at the shooting range

Spot a Skrull in disguise

Pilot the Helion ship

Hand-to-hand combat

Steal a secret file

Create an attack plan

YON-ROGG

VERS

MINN-ERVA

KORATH

BRON-CHAR

ATT-LASS

How could Vers surprise the enemy?

_____

STORYBOARD a scene for Captain Marvel. Draw in the boxes to show what happens when she lands on Planet Torfa.

Now colour your scenes!

A Skrull command has been intercepted, but the message is scrambled. Can you **DECODE** it?

A C ☐ I V ☐ T E

T H E

☐ T E A ☐ T H

B ☐ M B

S L O
A T

What alien do the missing letters spell?

_ _ _ _ _ _

Answers on **PAGE 48**

FILL THE GRID with these powers that take a hero to Super Hero.

FLIGHT

STRENGTH

SPEED

BLASTS

EYESIGHT

HEARING

AGILITY

If you could pick one super power, what would it be?

Answers on
PAGE 48

FOLLOW Captain Marvel's photon blasts through the maze to Talos! You can move one square at a time in ANY direction.

FINISH

Can you spot this yellow super symbol in the grid?

Answers on
PAGE 48

35

Captain Marvel is flying above the enemy!
Draw lines to match the **MISSING PIECES** to the picture.

Circle the piece that's not used
to complete the picture.

Answers on
PAGE 48

KREE versus SKRULL!

Play this game to see who
wins the galactic war.

* Decide who plays as 'stars' (Kree) and who plays as 'planets' (Skrull).
* Take turns to draw a star or a planet in a square.
* Whoever is the first to get three in a row wins!

Have more battles on a new sheet of paper.

COLOUR-SHIFT Talos, the alien spy, to his gruesome shade of green.

Who is he battling? Draw the hero.

Who's your STARFORCE alter ego?

Do you like to be the leader of a group?

- **A** Yes
- **B** Sometimes
- **C** Not really

Which of these colours do you like the most?

- **A** Black
- **B** Turquoise
- **C** Silver

Which of the below activities are you best at?

- **A** Computer games
- **B** Board games
- **C** Sports

Which of these annoys you the most?

- **A** Bad jokes
- **B** Being left out
- **C** Sitting still

Which of the below activities do you find the most fun?

- **A** Spot the difference
- **B** Mazes
- **C** Colouring in

Colour in your alter ego match!

Mostly As
MINN-ERVA

Mostly Bs
ATT-LASS

Mostly Cs
BRON-CHAR

Korath is sprinting into battle.
Can you **SPOT SIX DIFFERENCES** in the second picture?

Colour one Korath as a Kree
and the other in disguise!

40

Answers on
PAGE 48

The Helion ship carries Starforce all over the universe.
Design a new kind of **SPACE VEHICLE** for them!

NAME: _____

DESCRIPTION: _____

WEAPONS: _____

_____

Can you **SPOT** Talos hiding in this tangle of heroes?

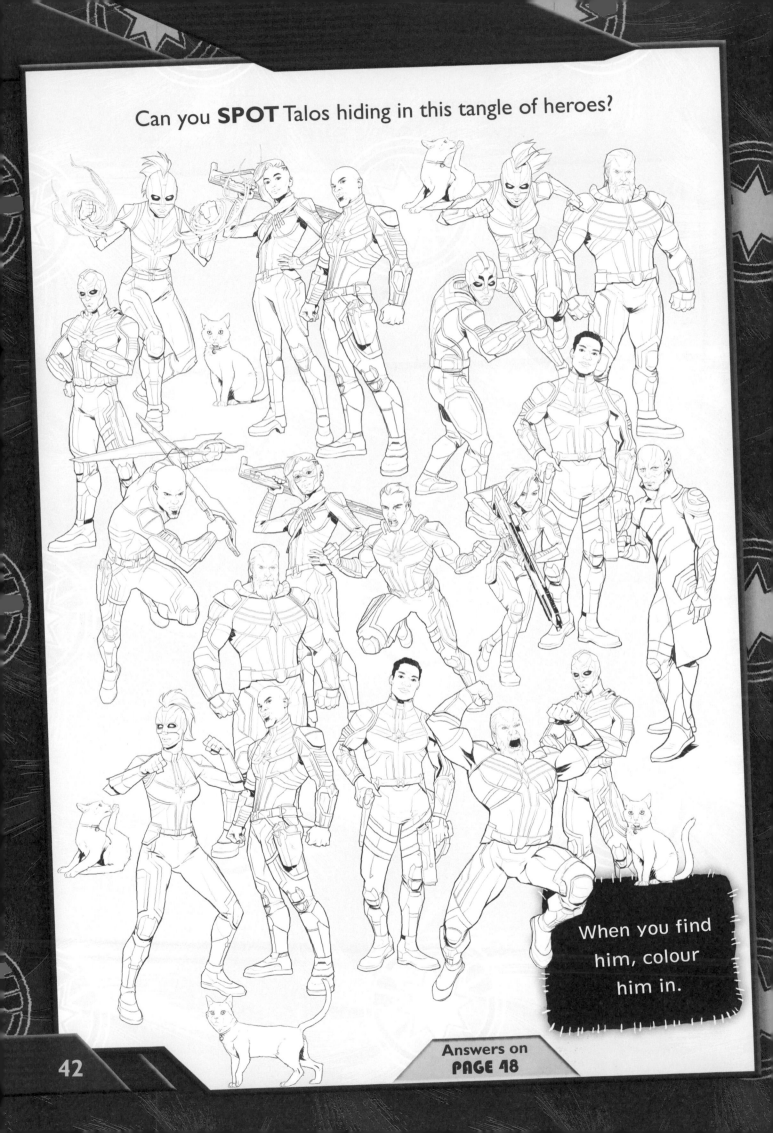

When you find him, colour him in.

Answers on **PAGE 48**

Are these shape-shifting statements TRUE or FALSE?

1 Minn-Erva was once a pilot.

2 Vers the Kree loves to run.

3 Korath is the commander of Starforce.

4 Skrulls wear turquoise uniforms.

5 Bron-Char is part of the Kree team.

Put a tick in the boxes under the statements that are true.

6 Starforce travel in the Helion ship.

7 Captain Marvel was once known as Carol Danvers.

8 Talos leads a group known as Skrullforce.

Answers on
PAGE 48

What could the letters of **STARFORCE** stand for?
Think of the band of heroes and write your word choices below.

S

T

A

R

F

O

R

C

E

Try doing
the same
with your
own name!

COLOUR Goose using the picture as a guide, or choose new cosmic colours of your own.

What type of animal
matches your personality?

_____

Captain Marvel gets help from her old friend Maria and Maria's daughter.

Reveal the daughter's name by writing the letter that comes **BEFORE** these in the alphabet.

L	P	O	J	D	B

Maria has the same job as Carol Danvers. What is it?

_____

Answers on **PAGE 48**

Captain Marvel has the same awesome **MOTTO** as she had as a pilot. Do you know what it is? Circle every second letter and write the letters in the boxes below.

START

☐☐☐☐☐☐ , ☐☐☐☐☐☐☐ ,

☐☐☐☐☐☐ !

Create your own Super Hero motto.

_____

ANSWERS:

PAGE 2:
1. Cat, 2. Torfa, 3. Alien,
4. Nick, 5. Kree, 6. Energy
7. Yon-Rogg, 8. Gravity

Captain Marvel's pilot name was Carol Danvers.

PAGE 4:

PAGE 6:
1. Korath, 2. Vers,
3. Att-Lass, 4. Minn-Erva,
5. Bron-Char, 6. Yon-Rogg

The secret to their success is TRAINING.

PAGE 7:

The cat's name is GOOSE.

PAGE 8:
SKRULL MOVING TOWARDS PLANET HALA

PAGE 9:
Korath

PAGE 10:

The full force number is 45.

PAGE 11:

PAGE 12:

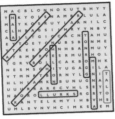

PAGE 13:
1. Map, 2. Cave, 3. Tale,
4. Near, 5. Learn, 6. Remain

PAGE 14:
The real Talos is F.

PAGE 15:
1. Green, 2. Air Force,
3. Leg, 4. Att-Lass,
5. Xandar, 6. Yon-Rogg

The letters spell GALAXY.

PAGE 16:
Bron-Char

PAGE 17:
Minn-Erva → Sniper
Att-Lass → Stealth expert
Vers → Energy blasts
Talos → Shape-shifting

The image is from Minn-Erva.

PAGE 20:
The answer is Minn-Erva.

There are 8 letters in her name.

PAGE 21:
Line D has an unbroken comms link.

KORATH receives the message.

PAGE 23:

VERS is missing.

PAGE 24:

PAGE 27:

PAGE 28:
14 Captain Marvels.

PAGE 30:

PAGE 33:
ACTIVATE THE STEALTH BOMB

The letters spell TALOS.

PAGE 34:

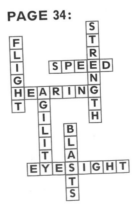

PAGE 35:

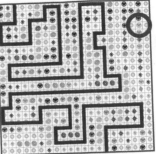

PAGE 36:

PAGE 40:

PAGE 42:

PAGE 43:
1. False, 2. True, 3. False,
4. False, 5. True, 6. True,
7. True, 8. False

PAGE 46:
Maria's daughter is called MONICA.

Maria is a pilot.

PAGE 47:
Captain Marvel's motto is HIGHER, FURTHER, FASTER.